Garden
Gates

DON STUART

❖ When Don Stuart was a child, he loved animals. His pets included toads, raccoons, and rabbits. These and other animals can be found in the garden he painted for this book cover. He has fun when he paints, and the creatures in the garden look like they are having fun, too!

Acknowledgments appear on pages 141-142, which constitute an extension of this copyright page.

ISBN 0-663-54651-6

4 5 6 7 8 9 10 VHP 98 97 96 95 94

New Dimensions
IN THE
WORLD OF READING

Garden Gates

P R O G R A M   A U T H O R S

James F. Baumann   Roselmina Indrisano   P. David Pearson
Theodore Clymer   Dale D. Johnson   Taffy E. Raphael
Carl Grant   Connie Juel   Marian Davies Toth
Elfrieda H. Hiebert   Jeanne R. Paratore   Richard L. Venezky

SILVER BURDETT GINN

NEEDHAM, MA   MORRISTOWN, NJ
ATLANTA, GA   DALLAS, TX   DEERFIELD, IL   MENLO PARK, CA

Unit 1 Theme

You Can Do It!

Unit 2 Theme

House and Home

You
Can Do It !

It sometimes takes
courage to try
something new.

Where does the
courage come from?

ROLLER SKATING, *bronze sculpture by Abastenia St. Leger Eberle, American, ca. 1906, Gift of Gertrude V. Whitney, Acq. # 31.15, Collection of Whitney Museum of American Art, New York*

Theme Books for
You Can Do It!

*D*o you sometimes have great ideas that make you want to leap out of your seat? People might say, "You can't do that! You're not old enough." What do you do then?

by Marilyn Sadler
Illustrated by Roger Bollen

❖ When Alistair builds a submarine, he discovers an exciting underwater world. Read *Alistair Underwater* by Marilyn Sadler and meet the frog people. How will Alistair save them from the huge Gooze?

❖ Grace loves to pretend. She has fun acting out all the parts of favorite stories. *Amazing Grace* by Mary Hoffman tells about Grace's dream to be Peter Pan in the school play. When others tell Grace that she can't be Peter Pan, how will she prove that she *can*?

More Books to Enjoy

The Bear Dance by Chris Riddell
Petunia by Roger Duvoisin
The Mixed-Up Chameleon
    by Eric Carle
Pierre by Maurice Sendak

FROG
AND
TOAD

from
Frog and Toad Together
written and illustrated by Arnold Lobel

Frog and Toad were reading a book
together. "The people in this book are brave,"
said Toad. "They fight dragons and giants, and
they are never afraid."

"I wonder if we are brave," said Frog. Frog
and Toad looked into a mirror.

"We look brave," said Frog.

"Yes, but are we?" asked Toad.

Frog and Toad went outside. "We can try to climb this mountain," said Frog. "That should tell us if we are brave."

Frog went leaping over rocks, and Toad came puffing up behind him. They came to a dark cave. A big snake came out of the cave.

"Hello lunch," said the snake when he saw
Frog and Toad. He opened his wide mouth.
Frog and Toad jumped away. Toad was shaking.
　　"I am not afraid!" he cried.
　　They climbed higher, and they heard a
loud noise. Many large stones were rolling
down the mountain.
　　"It's an avalanche!" cried Toad. Frog and
Toad jumped away. Frog was trembling.
　　"I am not afraid!" he shouted.

They came to the top of the mountain. The
shadow of a hawk fell over them. Frog and Toad
jumped under a rock. The hawk flew away.

"We are not afraid!" screamed Frog and
Toad at the same time. Then they ran down the
mountain very fast. They ran past the place
where they saw the avalanche. They ran past
the place where they saw the snake. They ran
all the way to Toad's house.

"Frog, I am glad to have a brave friend like you," said Toad. He jumped into the bed and pulled the covers over his head.

"And I am happy to know a brave person like you, Toad," said Frog. He jumped into the closet and shut the door.

Toad stayed in the bed, and Frog stayed in the closet. They stayed there for a long time, just feeling very brave together.

Reader's Response ∼ Do you think Frog and Toad were brave? Tell why.

Library Link ∼ *Look in your library for other books by Arnold Lobel, such as* Days with Frog and Toad, Frog and Toad All Year, *and* Frog and Toad Are Friends.

WHO'S THE FROG? WHO'S THE TOAD?

Suppose you meet a small green or brown fellow hopping along one day. How could you tell if it was a frog or a toad?

FROG

Both frogs and toads are amphibians, which means they live on land and in water. And both come in many sizes and colors.

Here are a few ways to tell them apart. Most frogs have smooth skin, but most toads have bumpy skin. Frogs spend more time in water, but toads spend more time on land. If you look inside a frog's mouth, you'll see a few teeth. But a toad has no teeth at all!

TOAD

So now you'll know whether to say "Hello, Frog" or "Hello, Toad" when one of them hops by.

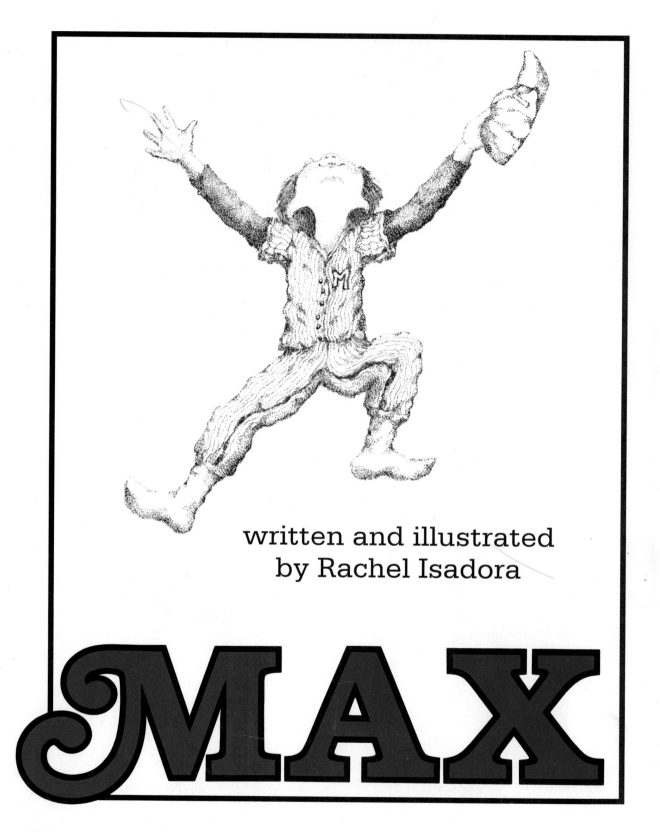

written and illustrated
by Rachel Isadora

MAX

Max is a great baseball player. He can run fast, jump high, and hardly ever misses a ball. Every Saturday he plays with his team in the park.

On Saturday mornings he walks with his sister Lisa to her dancing school. The school is on the way to the park.

One Saturday when they reach the school, Max still has lots of time before the game is to start. Lisa asks him if he wants to come inside for a while. Max doesn't really want to, but he says O.K.

21

Soon the class begins. He gets a
chair and sits near the door to watch.
The teacher invites Max to join
the class, but he must take off
his sneakers first.

He stretches at the barre.

He tries to do the split.

And the pas de chat. He is having fun.

Just as the class lines up to do leaps across the floor, Lisa points to the clock. It is time for Max to leave. Max doesn't want to miss the leaps. He waits and takes his turn. Then he must go.

He leaps all the way to the park.

He is late. Everybody is waiting for him.

He goes up to bat. Strike one! He tries again. Strike two! And then . . .

A home run!

Now Max has a new way to warm up for the game on Saturdays. He goes to dancing class.

Reader's Response ∼ Would you enjoy going to dancing class with Max? Tell why or why not.

DANCING...
THAT'S HARD WORK!

Max's sister is about nine or ten. That's when many ballet dancers begin taking lessons.

Some young dancers go to special schools where they practice every day. They learn how to do jumps and spins and other steps.

Dancers even practice on the days they perform. They are always working hard to become stronger and more graceful. Some lift weights or go swimming.

And if you want to be a dancer, get ready to buy a lot of shoes. Some dancers use ten pairs of dancing shoes in one week!

Dream Variation

by Langston Hughes

To fling my arms wide
In some place of the sun,
To whirl and to dance
Till the white day is done.
Then rest at cool evening
Beneath a tall tree
While night comes on gently,
    Dark like me—
That is my dream!

To fling my arms wide
In the face of the sun,
Dance! Whirl! Whirl!
Till the quick day is done.
Rest at pale evening . . .
A tall, slim tree . . .
Night coming tenderly
    Black like me.

27

The Ugly Duckling

by Hans Christian Andersen
retold by Karen-Amanda Toulon

It was a beautiful day in the country.
The sun shone on the green grass, and birds
flew in the bright blue sky. The air was full
of summer.

There was an old farmhouse not far
from a pond. The grass near this pond was
soft and tall. It was in this lovely place that
a mother duck had made her nest.

It was time for the mother duck to hatch her ducklings. What a long job it was! She had sat on her eggs for days and days. At last, one began to crack and out came a little yellow duckling. The other eggs began to hatch, too, and soon there were many little ducklings.

"Oh, what a big world this is!" said the ducklings. Now they had much more room to move than when they were in the eggs.

"Do you think this is the world?" said their mother. "Why, the world goes way past this nest, right into that garden over there! Now, let me see, are we all here?"

There was still one egg in the nest. "How much longer can this take?" she said. The mother duck sat down on the egg and waited some more. At last she heard a loud CRACK. A big gray duckling came out of the shell. It was very large and very ugly.

The ugly duckling looked at the mother duck and said, "Peep, peep, peep."

"You don't look like one of my ducklings," said the mother. "You're too big and gray." The ugly duckling made a sad peep.

"Well," said the mother, "we'll see about you. All ducks can swim. Let's see if you can." With that, the mother duck took all the ducklings down to the pond.

"You must be my duckling," said the proud mother to the ugly duckling. "Why, look how well you swim. Come. Let me show you to my friends," she said and took her ducklings to meet the other ducks.

The other ducks were not at all kind to the ugly duckling. "What a strange duckling!" they said. "Send him away! He's too ugly to be with us."

The ducks picked on the ugly duckling to no end. They bit his neck and legs. As time went on, things didn't get any better. The duckling felt so ugly and alone that he ran away.

The sad, little ugly duckling went very far. When night came, he saw a house. The door was open a bit, so he went in.

A woman lived in the house with her cat and her hen. When she saw the ugly duckling, she thought he could lay eggs like a hen.

"Now I'll have duck eggs," said the woman. She let the ugly duckling stay.

The cat and the hen were very hard to live with. They picked on the ugly duckling all of the time because he could not lay eggs like a hen or climb like a cat. Once again, the ugly duckling felt sad and alone.

One day the ugly duckling thought of how he missed the country. He thought of the bright sun and the lovely green grass. But more than anything, he wanted to be in the pond. He wanted to swim and feel the water all around him. He told the cat and the hen about it.

"How silly you are, you poor, ugly duckling," they said. "No one who is anything would want to be in water."

"You don't understand," said the
ugly duckling.

"Be quiet," said the cat, "and be glad
you have friends who can tell you what's
right. Just see to it that you lay some eggs
soon." The ugly duckling knew it was time
to leave the woman's house, so off he went.

Fall came. The leaves turned red and
yellow. Soon they fell off the trees and
began to blow about. The wind grew
stronger and stronger. The air grew colder
and colder.

One day the ugly duckling saw some big birds fly out from behind some trees. He had never seen such beautiful birds. They were white, with long, lovely necks and strong wings.

The ugly duckling watched them fly higher and higher into the air. He felt very strange. He didn't know what the birds were called or where they were going, but he felt so close to them in his heart. He wanted to be with them. As they flew away, the ugly duckling let out a sad cry. He would always remember those beautiful birds.

Winter came. It grew very, very cold. The duckling had to keep moving through the wind and the snow and the ice, so he would not freeze.

It would be too sad to tell all of the hard times the ugly duckling had that winter. Let's just say that the sun began to get warm again, and spring came at last.

One warm spring day, the duckling flew up into the air. His wings felt very strong. He had never gone so high or so fast. He felt proud. Soon he was flying over a lovely garden with a pond. In the pond were those beautiful, white birds he had seen before. When the ugly duckling saw them, he got that same strange feeling again.

"I must be near them," he thought. "I know they will not talk to me because I am so ugly. But I must go to them. They are so beautiful." And then he flew down to the pond.

The ugly duckling swam near the beautiful, white birds. They saw him and swam close to him. The poor duckling put his head down in shame because he thought he looked so ugly. But when he looked down, what did he see in the water? He saw a beautiful, white bird, not an ugly duckling. He was just like the others. He could not believe it was true.

Two children were playing in the garden. They called out with joy, "Look! Look at the new swan. He is the most beautiful swan of all."

Then three great swans came to the new swan and stroked him with their beaks. They, too, thought he was beautiful. He was proud and full of joy, for he had friends at last.

Reader's Response ~ Would you be a friend to the ugly duckling? Tell why or why not.

Library Link ~ *Hans Christian Andersen has written many stories for children. One story you may enjoy is called* The Nightingale.

Swans Take a Bow

There are several kinds of swans. Most are white, but some are black or a mixture of white and black.

The biggest swan is the trumpeter swan. When it spreads its wings, it can measure eight feet across.

Swans usually build nests by the water. Their babies are called cygnets. They can swim soon after they are born, but when they get tired, they often climb on their mother's or father's back for a little ride. Have you ever done that?

The Skating Lesson

by Johanna Hurwitz

Since November, Makiko Ogawa had gone ice-skating every Saturday. She always went with her friend Carmen and Carmen's brother, Luis. Luis was old enough to take the two girls skating in the park.

Makiko didn't have her own ice skates, so Luis lent her his old black skates. Makiko had to put on two pairs of socks so they would fit, but the skates worked well enough. She wished that she would get a pair of girl's white skates, like Carmen's, for her birthday.

The first time Makiko went skating she was scared. She thought she would fall. Luis taught her to look ahead, not down at her feet. When she looked ahead, she forgot she was wearing his old skates. Makiko loved to feel herself glide smoothly along on the ice.

Makiko went skating all winter. Each time she used Luis's old skates, she wished for a pair of her own.

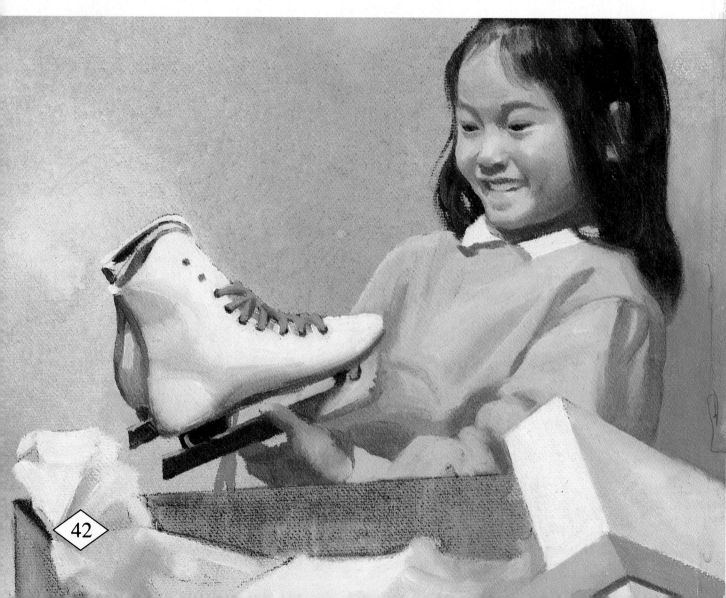

When Makiko's birthday came, there was a big box waiting for her. Makiko was afraid to look inside. Maybe it would not be what she really wanted.

Makiko slowly opened the box. Inside was a pair of white ice skates! They were just like Carmen's. Makiko gave her mother and father a big hug. She was very, very happy with her new skates. She couldn't wait to try them out.

The sun was bright and the air cold the next Saturday. There was no wind. It was a great day for skating, until Carmen called Makiko that morning.

"Luis and I can't go skating today," Carmen said. "Our grandmother is coming over. We want to stay here and visit with her."

Makiko was very upset. When Mrs. Ogawa saw how Makiko felt, she told her she would take her skating. "I know how much you want to try your birthday skates," her mother said. Makiko gave her mother a hug and ran and got her skates.

Many people were skating. Makiko rushed to put on her skates. She couldn't wait to get on the ice.

"Watch me," she called to her mother as she skated away. At first the new skates felt a little stiff and strange, but soon Makiko was skating smoothly. She waved to her mother. Mrs. Ogawa waved back. Makiko skated around and around. The next time Makiko saw her mother, she looked blue with cold. Makiko skated to the fence.

"We can't stay too much longer," said Mrs.
Ogawa. "I am so cold. I feel like I'm turning
to ice."

"Skate with me, and you won't be so
cold," Makiko said. "Skating keeps
you warm."

"I can't skate," said Mrs. Ogawa.
"Skating is for children."

"No, it isn't," said Makiko. "Look."
She pointed to a man and woman who were
skating past.

"I don't have any ice skates, Makiko," said Mrs. Ogawa.

"You can rent a pair," said Makiko. "A lot of people here are wearing rented skates. If Luis had not let me use his old skates, I would have rented them."

"Even if adults can skate and even if I rented skates, I still can't skate," said Mrs. Ogawa. "I don't know how."

Makiko had never thought of that. She thought her mother knew everything. "I could teach you," she said. "Luis taught me. Now I can teach you. It isn't hard."

"But the ice is very hard," said Makiko's mother, looking a little afraid.

"You won't fall. You can skate slowly, near the fence, and hold on when you need to," Makiko said. "I'll be right here."

Mrs. Ogawa thought about it. "Why not?" she said. "It does look like fun."

Soon Mrs. Ogawa was wearing a pair of skates for the first time. She walked slowly onto the ice, holding onto the fence as she moved. She was a bit shaky.

"Now, the first thing is to look ahead, not at your feet," Makiko said, thinking back to her first lesson with Luis. Very slowly the two of them moved together on the ice. Mrs. Ogawa took little steps, as if she were walking on the ice.

"Try not to walk when you skate," said Makiko. "Let your feet glide, one at a time. You want to move smoothly."

"I'm afraid," said Mrs. Ogawa, laughing at herself.

"I won't let you fall," Makiko said.
"Watch me." Makiko had never felt so big.

Then Makiko skated past her mother and
showed her how to look ahead and make her feet
glide over the ice. "Now you try," she said,
skating back to hold her mother's hand.

"I can't believe I'm doing this," laughed
Mrs. Ogawa.

"You're doing great!" said Makiko. "Do
you want ice skates for your birthday, too?"

They skated until it was time to go home for lunch. "Thank you for teaching me to skate," said Mrs. Ogawa. "It was a lot of fun. I'm glad I didn't fall, and I stayed warm, too."

"I never knew I could be a teacher," said Makiko. "It was fun." She thought of how many things her mother had taught her.

"Will you come skating with me next week, too?" asked Makiko.

"I think it's good for you to be with your friends," said her mother, "but how about this? Some night we will ask your father to come with us. You can teach him how to ice-skate, too. It must be beautiful skating under the stars."

As Mrs. Ogawa took back her rented skates, Makiko, deep in thought, watched the people skating. Today she was proud of many things. She was proud of her new skates, and she was proud of her skating. Most of all, she was proud of teaching her mother how to do something new. Makiko smiled a big smile and then ran to meet her mother.

Reader's Response ∼ Do you think Makiko was a good teacher? Tell why you think this.

Library Link ∼ *Look in the library for other books by Johanna Hurwitz, such as* New Neighbors for Nora *and* Russell Sprouts.

Tiffany Chin, Champion Skater

If Makiko practices very hard, how good a skater can she become? Here's what one skater named Tiffany Chin was able to do.

When she was eight, Tiffany got a pair of skates for a dollar at a garage sale.

When Tiffany first tried to skate, she fell down. But she really wanted to learn to skate well, so she worked hard and won her first contest. Then in 1984, she skated in the Winter Olympics. She came in fourth. She kept on practicing and became the 1985 United States champion—the best woman skater in her whole country.

Have you ever tried to do something that seemed very hard?

Keep the Lights Burning, Abbie

written by Peter and Connie Roop

illustrated by Peter E. Hanson

Abbie looked out the lighthouse window.
Waves washed up on the rocks below. Out at sea, a
ship sailed safely by.

"Will you sail to town today, Papa?"
Abbie asked.

"Yes," Captain Burgess answered. "Mama
needs medicine. The lights need oil. We need food.
The weather is good now. So it's safe to go out
in *Puffin.*"

"But what if you don't get back today?" asked
Abbie. "Who will take care of the lights?"

Papa smiled. "You will, Abbie."

"Oh, no, Papa!" said Abbie. "I have never done
it alone."

"You have trimmed the wicks before," said Papa. "You have cleaned the lamps and put in the oil. Mama is too sick to do it. Your sisters are too little. You must keep the lights burning, Abbie. Many ships count on our lighthouses."

Abbie followed Papa down the steps. Another day, she would have raced. This morning, her legs felt too heavy to run.

She and Papa walked down to the shore. Their little boat, *Puffin,* pulled on its rope. Captain Burgess jumped into the boat. He raised the sail. *Puffin* moved away from the shore.

"Keep the lights burning, Abbie!" her father called.

"I will, Papa," Abbie cried. But the wind carried off her words.

Abbie watched *Puffin* slide out to sea. Far away, she could see Matinicus Island. She knew Papa was a fine sailor. He could sail in rain. He could sail in fog. But if the wind blew up again, he could not sail back to Matinicus Rock today. The waves would be too high for the little boat. Then she would have to care for the lights.

Abbie looked up. The two lighthouse towers seemed as high as the sky. Her family's stone house sat between the towers. Not far away stood Abbie's henhouse.

Abbie went to feed her chickens. She threw some corn on the ground. The hungry hens hurried to it. Abbie sat on a rock and watched them.

"Now listen, Hope, Patience, and Charity," she said. "Don't eat it all too fast. There is not much corn left. But Papa will bring you more."

Abbie sighed. "I hope he gets home today. I am a little afraid to care for the lights alone."

Patience pecked Abbie's shoe. Hope turned her head. Charity ruffled her feathers. Abbie laughed.

"You three always make me feel better."

Abbie walked to the house. Esther opened the door.

"When is Papa coming back?" she asked.

"This afternoon," said Abbie.

"What if another storm starts?" asked Mahala.

"Don't worry," Abbie told her. "Papa will come back as soon as he can. You two run and get the eggs. How is Mama?" Abbie asked her sister Lydia.

"Still too sick to get up," Lydia answered. "It's a good thing Papa went today. Mama needs medicine. And we are running out of food."

"Then we must be careful," said Abbie. "If there is another storm, Papa will not get back today. We must make the food last."

That afternoon, Abbie helped Mahala write
her letters. Esther helped Lydia cook supper.
Everyone helped take care of Mama.

Outside, the sky turned gray. The wind put whitecaps on the waves. Another winter storm was coming.

When the sun went down, Abbie put on her coat. She had to light the lamps. Abbie ran up the lighthouse steps. She stopped at the top to look out. The waves were like big hills. The wind blew rain at the windows. She could not even see Matinicus Island. She knew Papa could not sail back. Abbie was afraid. She wished her brother, Benjy, were home. But he was away fishing. What if she could not light the lamps?

She picked up a box of matches. Her hands were shaking. She struck a match, but it went out. She struck another. This one burned.

Abbie held the match near the wick of the first lamp. The wick glowed. The light made Abbie feel better. One by one, she lit all the lamps. Then she went to the other lighthouse tower. She lit those lamps as well.

Out at sea, a ship saw the lights. It steered away from the dangerous rocks.

That night, the wind blew hard. Abbie could not sleep. She kept thinking about the lights. What if they went out? A ship might crash.

Abbie got out of bed. She put on her coat. She climbed the lighthouse steps. It was a good thing she had come. There was ice on the windows. The lights could not be seen.

All night long, Abbie climbed up and down. She scraped ice off the windows. She checked each light. Not one went out.

In the morning, the wind still blew. Waves rolled across Matinicus Rock. Abbie blew out each light. She trimmed each wick. She cleaned each lamp. She put in more oil. Then she went to breakfast. Then, at last, she went to bed.

For over a week, the wind and rain roared. For a while, the family had to move into one of the strong towers. One morning, water ran under the door.

"My chickens!" Abbie cried. "They will be washed away."

"Don't go outside," said Lydia. "You will be washed away, too."

Abbie picked up a basket.

"I go outside every night," she said. "I haven't been washed away yet."

She opened the door. Water splashed into the room. Abbie ran out into the rain. She waded to the henhouse. She put Patience under one arm. She pushed Hope and Charity into the basket. Just then she heard another big wave coming. It sounded like a train!

Abbie raced to the tower. "Open the door!" she yelled. Lydia opened the door. Abbie ran inside.

"Oh, look!" Mahala cried. "Look there! The sea is coming!"

The wave crashed over Matinicus Rock. It washed away the henhouse. The girls pushed the door shut. Then the wave hit it. Abbie felt the lighthouse shake. She was shaking, too. They had shut the door just in time.

Day after day, it snowed or rained. Abbie wished it would stop. She was tired of the wind. She was tired of the waves. She was tired of climbing the lighthouse steps. And she was tired of eggs. The only thing left to eat was eggs, and Abbie was sick of them.

Then one morning, the waves seemed smaller. The sky was not so black. The wind did not blow so hard.

Late that afternoon, the girls heard a voice outside. It was Papa. They ran to help him carry in the boxes. There was medicine for Mama. There was oil for the lamps. There was mail, and there was food. And there was corn for Abbie's chickens.

"I was afraid for you," said Papa. "Every night I watched for the lights. Every night I saw them. Then I knew you were all right."

Abbie smiled.

"I kept the lights burning, Papa."

Reader's Response ∿ Would you like to live on an island? Tell why or why not.

House and Home

Feeling at home is
a good feeling.

What makes people
feel at home?

A TRAMP ON CHRISTMAS DAY, *painting by Grandma Moses, American, c. 1946,*
Shelburne Museum, Shelburne, Vermont, © Grandma Moses Properties Co., New York

Theme Books for
House and Home

W*hen you think about home, what do you see? A house or an apartment? Or do you see a very different place?*

+ Zoe's home is more than just a house. Her home is fields, woods, and a big tower to climb. When you read **Zoe's Tower** by Paul and Emma Rogers, you will see what is special about Zoe's home.

Summertime Island is home to a boy in **Where Does the Trail Lead?** by Burton Albert. He will show you shells, birds, animals, and places forgotten long ago. You'll want to visit his special places again and again.

More Books to Enjoy

A House Is a House for Me by Mary Ann Hoberman
Evan's Corner by Elizabeth Starr Hill
The Little House by Virginia Lee Burton
Always Room for One More by Sorche Nic Leodhas

Not So Wise As You Suppose

by Michael Patrick Hearn

Once there was a farmer who went to the town wise man because he had a problem, and he did not know what to do. "How can I help you?" the wise man asked.

"I have a house with one small room," sighed the farmer.

"That is not a problem," the wise man said.

"It is a problem," the farmer sighed. "I live in this one small room with my wife and my seven children. We are always in one another's way, and we are always talking at the same time. It is so loud that I can hardly hear myself think. I cannot stand it any longer. Can you help me?"

The wise man stroked his chin and thought. "Do you have a horse?" the wise man asked.

"Yes, I have a horse," the farmer said.

"Then the answer is simple," the wise man said, "but you must do as I tell you. Tonight you must bring the horse into your house to stay with you, your wife, and your seven children." The farmer was surprised to hear such a plan, but he did as he was told.

The next morning he returned to the wise man. He was quite upset.

"You are not so wise as you suppose!" the farmer said. "Now my house is even louder. The horse just kicks and neighs morning, noon, and night! I cannot stand it any longer."

The wise man stroked his chin and thought. The farmer waited for him to speak.

"Do you have any cows?" asked the wise man.

"Yes, I have two cows," the farmer said.

"Then the answer is simple," the wise man said. "Tonight you must bring the cows into your house to stay with you, your wife, your seven children, and the horse."

"Are you sure?" the farmer asked. Surely the wise man did not mean what he was saying.

"Yes," said the wise man. "You must do as I tell you." So the farmer did as he was told.

The next morning the farmer returned to the wise man. He was even more upset.

"You are not so wise as you suppose!" the farmer said. "My house is louder than ever. The cows just moo morning, noon, and night, and the horse still kicks and neighs. I cannot stand it any longer."

The wise man stroked his chin and thought. The farmer waited for him to speak.

"Do you have any hens?" asked the wise man.

"Yes, I have some hens," said the farmer.

"Then the answer is simple," said the wise man. "Tonight you must bring the hens into your house to stay with you, your wife, your seven children, your horse, and your cows." The farmer could not believe his ears, but he did as he was told, for everyone knew the wise man to be very wise.

The next morning he returned to the wise
man. He was beside himself.

"You are not so wise as you suppose!" the
farmer said. "My house is louder than ever.
The hens just cluck and fight morning, noon,
and night! The cows still moo, and the horse
still neighs and kicks. My wife is upset, and the
children are crying. I cannot stand it any longer.
What can I do for some peace and quiet?"

"Well, take the animals out of your house,"
the wise man said. So the farmer did as he
was told, and once more he returned to the
wise man.

"You *are* as wise as you suppose!" the farmer said. "You have turned my house into a home again! Now with all of the animals out, it is so nice and quiet! My family is happy, and I can hear myself think again. You have taught me to be happy with my house just the way it is. Thank you, thank you."

And the wise man smiled.

Reader's Response ∼ How would you have helped the farmer solve his problem?

The Wise People of Chelm

There once was a town in Europe called Chelm, where the people thought they were very wise. Here is a story that is told about them:

The tailor in Chelm thought the sun was more important than the moon. "Don't be silly," said his wife. "The moon is much more important."

Soon a teacher came in to have his coat fixed. They asked him, "Which is more important, the sun or the moon?"

"Listen, my friends," he began after a long silence, "the moon is more important. You see, the moon shines at night when it's dark, so we need it more. The sun only shines during the day, when there is plenty of light already."

You decide. Are the people of Chelm as wise as they suppose?

Houses

by Aileen Fisher

Houses are faces
(haven't you found?)
with their hats in the air,
and their necks in the ground.

Windows are noses,
windows are eyes,
and doors are the mouths
of a suitable size.

And a porch—or the place
where porches begin—
is just like a mustache
shading the chin.

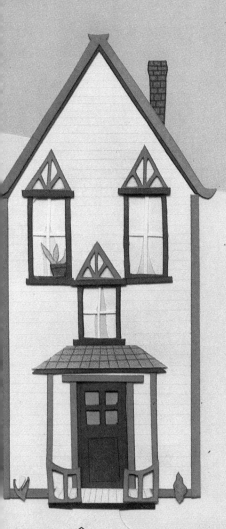

77

Pueblos
of the Southwest

by Anna Westcott

Some Native Americans who live in the Southwest got their name from the kind of homes and villages they built. Their villages were made of houses that were joined together to make big buildings.

Long ago, Spanish people came upon the villages of these Native Americans. The Spanish people used the word *pueblo* to name these villages. The word *pueblo* is a Spanish word meaning "village." The Native Americans who lived in these villages became known as the Pueblo people.

Pueblo buildings had many homes that were joined together. The first ones were built nearly seven hundred years ago. Most Pueblo buildings were two or three stories high. They were made from things that the people could find in the dry lands of the Southwest, such as earth, stone, and some wood. The Pueblo people used ladders to get into their own houses and to get to the other homes in the large Pueblo village.

How Pueblo Homes Were Made

When a new home was added on to the pueblo, the family built its house using the old ways. The Pueblo men built the walls of the house with stone and mud. They had to cut the stone and put it in place. By putting stones one on top of the other, they built the walls. The mud held the stones together. Then the men put wood on top of the walls to start the flat roof.

80

The Pueblo women finished the house. They covered the wood on the roof with poles, leaving an opening. The family would use this opening to get into the house. Next, the women covered the poles with branches and grasses. Then they covered the roof with mud. When the mud was dry, the women covered the roof with earth. Then they covered the stone walls with clay.

The Pueblo family joined their new home to the home of the woman's mother and father. When the other girls in the family grew up, they also built new homes and joined them together. In this way, the homes made one big building.

When the Pueblo people joined their homes together, they left a space in the middle for everyone to share. They called this space the plaza. When they looked down from their roof, the family could see everything in the plaza. From the roof, they could watch the dances the people did at special times.

Inside a Pueblo Home

A Pueblo family went into their home by climbing down through the opening on the roof, using a ladder. Once inside, there would be just one room for the family to share. This one room was used mainly for sleeping, because most of a Pueblo family's time was spent outside. There were no tables, chairs, or beds. The family used blankets, rugs, and sheepskins for sitting and sleeping. A fireplace kept the room warm.

The most important thing found in a Pueblo home was the woman's grinding stone. The woman used the grinding stone to crush corn and other foods for cooking.

Feathers were also important to the Pueblo people. The men put four feathers on the ground before building the walls of a house. People also hung feathers in their homes. They believed that the feathers would help to keep them safe.

Pueblos Today

Pueblo villages today are different from those of long ago. Today you can see Pueblo homes that are one or two stories high. They also have many rooms. These newer homes have doors and windows, too. They are a lot like the homes you live in.

Some Pueblo people have moved away from their villages. They have built homes in the city near their work. Although they have moved away, the Pueblo people still feel that village life is important. They return to their pueblo to take part in village life and in the special Pueblo dances held in the plaza.

Reader's Response ～ What would be the best thing about living in a Pueblo home? Tell why you think this.

84

The People
Who Went Before

Before the Pueblo people, there were other Native Americans called Anasazi, which is a Navajo word that means "enemy ancestors."

Some Anasazi built beautiful towns in the cliffs of canyons. They built their houses much like the Pueblo people. They built them one on top of another so many people lived close together.

Do you think you would like living in one of these cliff homes?

One of the Anasazi's oldest towns is called Mesa Verde. Today it is a national park in Colorado. Now anyone can go there and learn about the Anasazi and the way they lived.

Home

from *In My Mother's House*

by Ann Nolan Clark

This is my Mother's house;
My Father made it.
He made it with adobe bricks;
He made it strong;

He made it big;
He made it high;
My Mother's house,
I live in it.

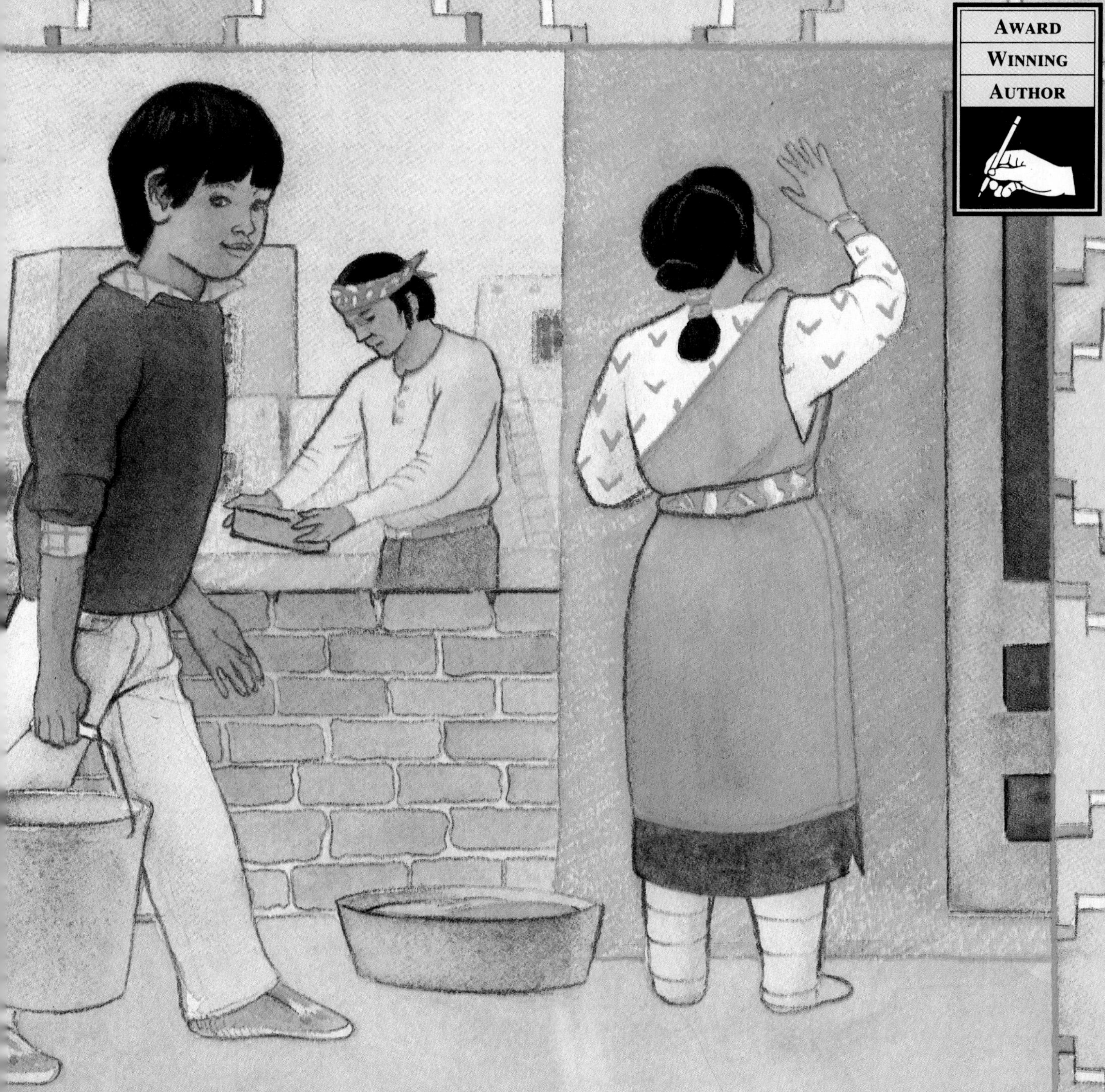

This is my Mother's house;

My Mother plastered it

With brown clay;

On the outside

My Mother plastered it.

The inside walls are white;
My Mother made them white;
The floor is smooth;
My Mother made it smooth,
For me to live there.

In my Mother's house
There is a fireplace:
The fireplace holds the fire.
On dark nights the fire is bright;
On cold nights the fire is warm.
The fire is always there,
To help me see,
To keep me warm.

In my Mother's house
There are the grinding stones:
The big, flat holding stone,
The small rubbing stone;
The grinding stones,
My Mother's grinding stones.

On the floor
Beside her stones
My Mother kneels,
And with her hands
She grinds the corn;
Yellow corn and blue corn
My Mother grinds
For me to eat.

Red chili and meat and melons
And yellow cornmeal
I have to eat.

Apricots and peaches
And little red plums
I have to eat.

Big round tortillas
And brown frijoles
I have to eat.
I eat them;
I like them.

In my Mother's house
All day
I play and work;
All night
I sleep.

The walls come close around me
In a good way.
I can see them;
I can feel them;
I live with them.

This house is good to me,
It keeps me;
I like it,
My Mother's house.

Reader's Response ∼ If you were
to write a poem about your home,
what things would you tell about?

A Writer and Teacher

How do you think Ann Nolan Clark began writing stories for children?

A long time ago, Ms. Clark was asked to be a teacher in a one-room country school in New Mexico. She found out that the school was very poor. The children, who were Native Americans, had very few books to read.

What would you have done?

Ann Nolan Clark began to write her own books for the children. "Home" is part of a poem she wrote with the help of some of her students. She wanted them to be able to read about themselves and their own people.

Ms. Clark's books help children everywhere learn about the way of life of the Pueblo people.

A Smooth Move
by Berniece Rabe

March 25

    I am Gus, and this is my journal. For a long time, I've lived with my mom, my dad, my little brother, Lee, and my cat, Ki-Ki, in a long, low house near Portland, Oregon. Now my dad has a new job in Washington, D.C., and we have to move. I'm not sure I like that. I know I'll miss my friends. But I have to be brave. Mom said keeping a journal might help.

April 2

Dad's already moved to Washington, D.C., to start his job. We talk to him on the phone, and today we got a letter. He says he misses us . . .

He sent pictures of our new, tall house. My bedroom will be on the third floor. That sounds neat! Most of the time, I want to go to Washington, D.C. I miss my dad very much.

April 13

Our house finally sold! Mom is very happy. Some strangers with three kids bought it. The biggest girl will get my bedroom. Dad laughed on the telephone. He said, "Hey, Gus, that came off smooth! Wait until you see your new, tall school—it's standing up on end!" I tried to laugh, too. I really do like to laugh. But I don't know if I'll like a tall school.

April 14

Today my good friends Thad and Jane and Paul walked with me for the last time to my long, low school. I was sad, but Paul told me a joke I hadn't heard: "Where do penguins keep their money? In a snow bank!" That made me laugh.

My teacher gave me my report card to take to my new school. It was a great report card, except for one line: "Gus is a good student, but he is a talker." I sure didn't feel like laughing when I read *that.* This move won't be so smooth when my new teacher finds out I'm a talker!

April 15

I dreamed that I went all alone to the new school. The teacher read my report card out loud. Everyone laughed. I felt awful. I don't like strangers laughing at me. I was glad to wake up still in Portland. But the sign in our front yard says "Sold," so we have to move.

Mom gave me a list of things to do:

1. Put clothes you will need right away into your big suitcase.
2. Pack two favorite toys.
3. Pack two favorite books.
4. Put toys into toy box.

I added:

5. Get friends' addresses.
6. Take journal on plane.

April 16

Men came to pack our things into big boxes. That did not go smooth. They came too early! While Mom was in Lee's room changing his diaper, they packed the leftover bread dough she was going to bake!

I said, "Hey, you'd better not do that!" They didn't pay any attention to me. Then they packed dirty dishes from the sink and clothes from the washer— still dripping wet! I laughed when I told Mom, but she didn't laugh.

All the furniture and all the boxes went into a big moving van. We waved goodbye to the men as they drove away. Mom sighed as she looked at the messy floors.

"Things could be worse," I said. "The bread dough could rise and rise and rise until all our toys and furniture are covered. I know it could happen. I know all about yeast."

Mom said, "Gus, don't be such a worrier. Go and get ready for the slumber party tonight."

April 17

Slumber parties are great! Thad and Jane and Paul brought hot chocolate, black licorice strings, nacho chips, flashlights, and sleeping bags. Mom's friends came with pizza, cans of pop, a broom, and some toilet paper. Everyone stayed to sleep over in our empty house. It seemed strange and spooky with no furniture. My friends and I told jokes all night long.

But in the morning we had to say goodbye to our long, low house and our friends. Mom cried. I did, too, and so did Lee. Ki-Ki meowed in her travel carrier.

Thad and his mom took us to the airport. They promised to write. We promised to write back. We all waved and waved.

April 17 (*written on an airplane*)

When we took off, I could see Mt. St. Helens and Mt. Hood. Now I can just see clouds. We're really high—flying from the west coast of the United States of America to the east coast of the United States of America. Ki-Ki is in her cat carrier under Mom's seat. I told the flight attendant about Ki-Ki and about our old house and our new house and all about yeast.

So far, I've played word games with Mom and tickled Lee in the ribs. And I've talked to other passengers. We ate lunch from a tray on the seat back. Smooth going. Well, not quite. I'll have to stop writing now. Ki-Ki is howling. She wants to get out.

Still April 17 (*still in airplane*)

I put my hand inside the carrier and talked soft and sweet to Ki-Ki till she purred. The captain announced, "We're now crossing the Mississippi River. Visibility is good." I looked out the window and saw a wide river and some very flat country. Mom showed me a big map in the airline magazine. I found the Mississippi River on it.

"We've flown right over the moving van," Mom said. "It had a headstart, but we'll beat it to the east coast. We'll live in a hotel for three days until the van comes with our furniture."

MISSISSIPPI RIVER

Late on April 17

At five o'clock, Dad met us at the gate. I hugged him hard. Then I told him, "Your watch is wrong. We left Portland more than six hours ago. It's two o'clock." Dad explained to me about time zones. It's three hours later on the east coast than on the west coast. That's because the earth is turning away from the sun. I really like being with Dad again.

And the hotel is great! It has a pool and a game room. My brother has a crib, my parents have one king-sized bed, and I get the other king-sized bed all to myself. Ki-Ki's bed is under my bed, and she's been growling a lot. I said, "Give her tuna. She never growls if she has tuna. Dry cat food is for the birds!"

"Well, hardly," Dad said, but he fed Ki-Ki tuna. She purred.

April 20

 It's been three days, and the moving van hasn't come. We keep feeding Ki-Ki more and more tuna. It smells. Mom said she's tired of the hotel, but I like it. I ride up and down the elevator with Ki-Ki and talk to people. I get soda pop and peanuts from the machines. We all swim in the pool and play in the game room.

April 22

Today we got bad news. The moving van is stalled in Utah. It won't come for another week. I wonder if the bread dough rose until it covered the engine?

Mom gave a deep sigh. Lee pulled Ki-Ki's tail.

"Let's all try to be patient and happy," Dad said.

So I rode the elevator one hundred times today. I told lots of people about the bread dough and how it had probably covered all our furniture. They all thought that was pretty funny. I laughed, too.

Dad said he likes to hear me laugh. Mom said I was being a good sport and making this difficult move go as smooth as possible.

April 24

We still sleep nights at the hotel. But during the days, we explore our new house. Dad was right—it is tall! There are lots of stairs. I like my new room up in the treetops.

Ki-Ki hid from us. I was the one who found her. That's how I learned all the hiding places.

April 26

We went to see my new school today. It's very tall, too, with three fire escapes. I'd like to climb all three, but I won't. There are lots of kids on the playground.

I said, "I might not like it. I don't know anyone here."

"A talker like you, Gus?" Dad said. "You won't have trouble making friends."

He may be right. But what if my new teacher doesn't like talkers?

April 29

The big moving van made it at last! Joseph, a boy my age, came to watch. I told him all about the rising bread dough. He thought it was pretty funny, and he could hardly wait to see it.

Well, the dishes were crusted over. And Ki-Ki's nose did a lot of twitching when she went near the dirty laundry. The yeast dough was hard as a rock. It hadn't risen at all. The temperature wasn't warm enough. I learned some more about yeast.

"What made this van stall in Utah?" I asked the driver.

"A mud slide blocked the road," he told me.

Mom dashed out with money for ice cream bars for me and my new friend, if I promised not to bother the men. I promised, and everything got unloaded. So moving-in day went smooth as ice cream.

May 2

I rode to school today with Joseph, on a yellow bus. But I didn't tell him any jokes. I didn't say much at all. I just held onto my report card that says I am a talker. I held onto it inside my shirt.

My new teacher is short—a short teacher in a tall school! That's pretty funny, and I told her so. She smiles just like my old teacher. So I told her about the bread dough. She laughed.

She took me to the media center, and I found two of my favorite books there. Then she said, "I'll look at your report card while you check out your books." She held out her hand. I hoped she'd forgotten about it. I pulled out my report card from under my shirt and held my breath.

"Um-m-m," she said, "I do enjoy a good talker. Talkers make good storytellers." She smiled at me. Then I laughed. I mean I *really* laughed! Everything was smooth sailing after that.

Still May 2

Going home on the bus today, I asked Joseph and some other kids, "Where do penguins keep their money?" No one knew, so I said, "In a snow bank!" They laughed. Then they told me some jokes I hadn't heard before, and we all sang some pretty silly songs.

But later, I got to missing my old friends. I wished I could show them my new house and tall school. Our family went out for pizza again, same as last night. It's a terrific pizza place we've found. I love pizza. I wish my old friends could see this new pizza place.

May 8

Today Dad took us to see the White House and the pandas at the National Zoo. Living in Washington, D.C., is neat!

May 10

    This will be the last page in my
moving journal. I'll write a whole page
letter to my Portland friends. I know just
what I'll say. I'll say,

Dear Thad, Jane, and Paul,
    Our whole move went real smooth. We
have a big, beautiful country. I know.
I flew over all of it.
    Come visit Washington, D.C. I'll take
you to see where the President of the
entire United States of America lives.
Come see my new, tall house and meet
my new friends.
    Heard any new jokes? Write back
real soon. I miss you. But I think
I'm going to like it here.

                GUS

Reader's Response 〜 What would
make a move "smooth" for you?

THE MAGIC OF YEAST

Gus sure thought a lot about yeast. But what is yeast? And what does it do?

Yeast is a tiny living plant. When a cook mixes a small amount of yeast with flour, water, and other ingredients and puts the mixture in a warm place, a magical thing happens. It begins to expand and grow. And if the mixture is put in the oven and baked awhile— PRESTO! It becomes bread.

Bread is made in countries all over the world—sometimes with yeast and sometimes without it. What do you think would be different about bread made without yeast?

The House That Nobody Wanted

from *Junk Day on Juniper Street*
written by Lilian Moore
illustrated by Arnold Lobel

There was once a little house that stood
on a hill.

It was an old house—very old and very
gray. It had gray doors and gray windows, gray
walls and a gray fence.

A little old man and a little old woman
lived in this house. And they had lived there
for a long time.

112

The old man and the old woman did not go out much. But one fine day they made up their minds to visit their friends.

So they got into their little old car and rode away. They rode uphill and downhill and then uphill and downhill again.

And at last they saw the house of their
friends. It was a little red house with white
doors and windows, and all around it flowers
and green things were growing.

The little old man and the little old
woman had a good time with their friends.

Then they got into their little old car and
went home. They rode uphill and downhill,
then uphill and downhill again.

And at last they came to their own house.

"My!" said the old woman. "Our house is
very gray, isn't it?"

"And there is nothing green to see when we look out," said the old man.

"Old man, let's sell this house!" said the old woman. "Then we can buy a pretty house!"

". . . with grass and flowers growing around it!" said the old man.

So the little old man and the little old woman tried to sell their house.

First a man came to look.

"No," he said. "This house is too gray for me. I like a red house."

And he went away.

"Oh dear!" said the little old woman.

"Let's paint the house red," said the old man. "Then maybe the next one will buy it."

So the little old man and the little old woman painted the house red.

Soon after, a woman came to look.

"I like a house that has white windows and white doors," she said. "I like a white fence and a white gate, too." And she went away.

So the little old man and the little old woman painted the windows white. Then they painted the doors and the gate and the fence white, too.

Soon after that, a man and a woman
came to see the house. They liked the outside.

"But it is so gray inside," said the woman.

And they went away.

So this time the little old man and the
little old woman painted the walls inside the
house. They painted some walls yellow and
some walls blue.

Soon another man came to see the house.

"This is a pretty house," he said. "But I am
looking for a home with a garden."

And he, too, went away.

The old man and the old woman began to
work on a garden.

Soon green grass was growing.

Then one day there were flowers—red and purple and yellow—growing all around the house.

"Now," said the old woman. "Someone will want to buy this house! Then at last we can buy the house *we* want."

The old man looked around.

"Old woman," he said. "What kind of house *do* we want?"

"Well," she said. "We want a pretty house."

"Painted inside and out?" he asked.

"Oh yes!" said the old woman.

"With grass and flowers growing around it?" asked the old man.

"Oh yes!" said the little old woman.

The old man laughed.

"Look around, old woman!" he told her.

So the little old woman looked around.

She saw a red house with white windows and doors, a white fence and a white gate, too.

Inside the house she saw bright yellow and blue walls.

Outside she saw grass and flowers growing.

"Well!" she said, surprised. "This is a pretty house, isn't it?"

"This is just the house we want!" said the old man.

So the little old man and the little old woman went right on living in the little old house on the hill.

Only it wasn't a little gray house anymore.

Reader's Response ~ What would you have done to fix up the little gray house?

Library Link ~ *You might enjoy reading the rest of the stories in the book* Junk Day on Juniper Street.

GLOSSARY

Full pronunciation key* The pronunciation of each word is shown just after the word, in this way: **abbreviate** (ə brē′vē āt).

The letters and signs used are pronounced as in the words below.

The mark ′ is placed after a syllable with primary or heavy accent as in the example above.

The mark ′ after a syllable shows a secondary or lighter accent, as in **abbreviation** (ə brē′vē ā′shən).

SYMBOL	KEY WORDS	SYMBOL	KEY WORDS	SYMBOL	KEY WORDS
a	ask, fat	u	up, cut	r	red, dear
ā	ape, date	ur	fur, fern	s	sell, pass
ä	car, father			t	top, hat
		ə	a in ago	v	vat, have
e	elf, ten		e in agent	w	will, always
er	berry, care		e in father	y	yet, yard
ē	even, meet		i in unity	z	zebra, haze
			o in collect		
i	is, hit		u in focus	ch	chin, arch
ir	mirror, here			n̂g	ring, singer
ī	ice, fire	b	bed, dub	sh	she, dash
		d	did, had	th	thin, truth
o	lot, pond	f	fall, off	*th*	then, father
ō	open, go	g	get, dog	zh	s in pleasure
ô	law, horn	h	he, ahead		
oi	oil, point	j	joy, jump	′	as in (ā′b′l)
oo	look, pull	k	kill, bake		
o͞o	ooze, tool	l	let, ball		
yoo	unite, cure	m	met, trim		
yo͞o	cute, few	n	not, ton		
ou	out, crowd	p	put, tap		

*Pronunciation key and respellings adapted from *Webster's New World Dictionary, Basic School Edition,*

Copyright © 1983 by Simon & Schuster, Inc. Reprinted by permission.

A

a·do·be (ə dō′bē) brick made of sun-dried clay: "The house was made of *adobe*."

a·dults (ə dults′ *or* ad′ults) **1.** grown-ups. **2.** men or women who are grown up: "The children stood in front of the *adults*."

a·fraid (ə frād′) frightened: "He is *afraid* of bees."

a·head (ə hed′) in the front or to the front: "Katie was *ahead* of me in line."

a·long (ə lông′) on or beside: "We walked *along* the road."

al·though (ôl *thō*′) **1.** even if. **2.** in spite of the fact that: "He fell *although* he was careful."

an·swer (an′sər) **1.** a reply to a question: "Your *answer* to the question is correct." **2.** the way to solve a problem.

a·pri·cots (ap′rə kots *or* a′prə kots) pale orange fruit similar to peaches but smaller: "We like to put *apricots* in the fruit salad."

av·a·lanche (av′ə lanch) large mass of snow or rocks sliding very fast down a mountain: "The *avalanche* covered the mountain road."

adobe

barre

B

barre (bär) French word for a railing used by ballet dancers: "She held onto the *barre* as she stretched her leg."

base·ball (bās′bôl) **1.** a game played using a ball and bat by two teams of nine players each: "Pedro watched his sister play *baseball*." **2.** the ball used in the game.

baseball team

climb

closet

coast

be·side (bi sīd′) **1.** by or next to. **2.** upset: "She was *beside* herself with worry."

brave (brāv) **1.** not afraid: "Ben was *brave* during the storm." **2.** a Native American warrior.

built (bilt) constructed; made by putting together parts or materials: "He *built* the house with red bricks."

C

chil·dren (chil′drən) young boys and girls: "The *children* go to school."

chi·li (chil′ē) a Mexican food made with ground beef, red peppers, spices, and beans: "We ate a big bowl of *chili* with our corn bread."

class (klas) **1.** a group of people or things that are alike in some ways. **2.** a group of students that meet together: "My dance *class* meets on Saturday mornings."

climb (klīm) go up or down using feet and sometimes hands: "I like to *climb* trees."

clos·et (kloz′it) a small room or cupboard: "My *closet* is big enough to hold all my clothes."

coast (kōst) **1.** the land along the seashore: "We went for a ride along the California *coast*." **2.** a slide or ride downhill, as on a sled.

corn·meal (kôrn′mēl) grain made from crushed corn: "Vera used *cornmeal* when she made corn bread."

cov·ered (kuv′ərd) placed one thing over another: "The mother *covered* the sick child with a warm blanket."

D

danc·ing (dans′ing) **1.** moving the body and feet in a kind of rhythm, usually to music. **2.** a word to describe a place where dancing takes place: "The children had fun in their *dancing* class."

dif·fer·ent (dif′ər ənt *or* dif′rənt) not alike; not the same as: "I am *different* from my sister."

dough (dō) a mixture of flour and other things used to bake bread and cookies: "We mixed the *dough* with a spoon."

drag·ons (drag′ənz) make-believe monsters that look like big lizards and breathe fire and smoke: "The *dragons* in the story scared me."

duck·ling (duk′ling) a young duck: "The *duckling* stayed close to its mother."

dragon

E

earth (urth) **1.** the planet we live on. **2.** the ground or soil: "I dug for worms in the *earth*."

e·ven (ē′vən) **1.** flat; smooth. **2.** though it may seem unlikely: "*Even* a baby can do that."

F

fa·vor·ite (fā′vər it) best liked: "My *favorite* sport is swimming."

duckling

feather

giant

grinding stone

feath·ers (fe*th*′ərz) soft, light parts covering the body of a bird: "The bird lost its *feathers*."

fight (fīt) **1.** battle; struggle: "The boys *fight* over who goes first." **2.** work hard to try to overcome.

fin·ished (fin′isht) came to an end: "I *finished* all my homework."

floor (flôr) the flat bottom part of a room on which to walk: "My wet shoes squeaked as I walked across the *floor*."

fri·jol·es (frē hōl′ēz) any bean, especially the kidney bean, used in many Mexican and southwestern United States foods: "Rosa added *frijoles* to the spicy chili."

G

gi·ants (jī′ənts) make-believe beings that look like people but are much bigger and stronger: "The *giants* in the story could move a house."

glide (glīd) move along smoothly and easily: "We watched the skater *glide* along the ice."

grew (grōō) **1.** became larger or taller. **2.** became: "I *grew* tired by the end of the day."

grind·ing stone (grīnd′iṅg stōn′) a flat, rounded stone used to crush foods: "The woman used a *grinding stone* to grind the corn into cornmeal."

a	fat	**oi**	oil	**ch**	chin
ā	ape	**oo**	look	**sh**	she
ä	car, father	**ōō**	tool	**th**	thin
e	ten	**ou**	out	***th***	then
er	care	**u**	up	**zh**	leisure
ē	even	**ʉr**	fur	**n̂g**	ring
i	hit				
ir	here	**ə** =	a *in* ago		
ī	bite, fire		e *in* agent		
o	lot		i *in* unity		
ō	go		o *in* collect		
ô	law, horn		u *in* focus		

H

hawk (hôk) a large bird that eats smaller birds and other animals: "A *hawk* has very sharp eyesight."

heart (härt) **1.** a muscle that pumps blood through the body. **2.** the center. **3.** the human heart, thought of as something with feelings such as love, kindness, and sadness: "He gave to others because he had a kind *heart*."

her·self (hər self′) **1.** her own self: "She hurt *herself*." **2.** her usual self.

high·er (hī′ər) above: "If I stand on this ladder, I will be *higher* than you."

ho·tel (hō tel′) a building where travelers can rent rooms and buy meals: "We stayed in a big *hotel*."

hawk

J

joined (joind) connected together: "The islands were *joined* by a bridge."

jokes (jōks) funny stories: "We laughed at the *jokes* she told."

jour·nal (jʉr′nəl) a daily record of what happens: "Mary kept a *journal* of her trip."

joy (joi) **1.** a happy feeling: "Watching him in the class play brought *joy* to his parents." **2.** anything that causes this feeling.

journal

K

kneels

kneels (nēlz) rests on a knee or knees: "He *kneels* to dig in the sand."

L

ladders

lad·der (lad′ər) a frame for climbing up or down: "We climbed the *ladder* to reach the roof."

large (lärj) of great size: "The box was so *large* I was able to hide behind it."

les·son (les″n) something to be learned, as by a student: "I have a piano *lesson* this afternoon."

loud (loud) **1.** not quiet: "A *loud* noise woke me." **2.** noisy.

love·ly (luv′lē) beautiful; pleasing in looks or character: "The garden was *lovely* when the flowers bloomed."

M

mountain

moun·tain (moun′t′n) a very high hill: "We walked to the top of the *mountain*."

mouth (mouth) the opening on the face that a person uses for talking or eating: "I opened my *mouth* wide so the dentist could look at my teeth."

N

a fat	oi oil	ch chin
ā ape	oo look	sh she
ä car, father	o͞o tool	th thin
e ten	ou out	*th* then
er care	u up	zh leisure
ē even	ur fur	ṉg ring
i hit		
ir here	ə = a *in* ago	
ī bite, fire	e *in* agent	
o lot	i *in* unity	
ō go	o *in* collect	
ô law, horn	u *in* focus	

neighs (nāz) whinnies; makes sounds like those of a horse: ''The horse *neighs* when he sees me.''

noise (noiz) sound, especially a loud, unpleasant sound: ''We made too much *noise*.''

noon (no͞on) twelve o'clock in the daytime: ''We eat lunch at *noon*.''

No·vem·ber (nō vem′bər) the eleventh month of the year: ''*November* is the month after October.''

P

park

park (pärk) **1.** a place with trees, grass, and benches where people go to rest or play: ''We play ball in the *park*.'' **2.** to leave a car or other vehicle in a certain place for a time.

pas de chat (pä′ də shä′) French phrase for a kind of ballet step: ''The dance teacher taught us to do a *pas de chat*.''

pa·tient (pā′shənt) **1.** able to put up with things like delay, boredom, or pain: ''Be *patient*! The bus will be here soon.'' **2.** a person being cared for by a doctor.

peace (pēs) **1.** freedom from war or fighting. **2.** calm or quiet: ''They were at *peace*.''

peach·es (pēch′iz) round, juicy, pinkish-yellow fruit with fuzzy skin and a rough pit: ''We ate *peaches* with our lunch.''

pas de chat

points

proud

pueblo

pen·guins (peńg′gwinz) sea birds that live in the antarctic where there is snow all year long: "*Penguins* swim, but cannot fly."

piz·za (pēt′sə) food made by baking a thin layer of dough covered with tomatoes, cheese, and spices: "We each ate a piece of *pizza*."

plas·tered (plas′tərd) covered with a mixture used for coating walls or ceilings: "She *plastered* the kitchen wall."

play·er (plā′ər) a person who plays a game or musical instrument: "Each *player* on the team is important."

pla·za (plä′zə *or* plaz′ə) a public area or square: "They danced in the *plaza*."

plums (plumz) juicy fruit with dark, smooth skin and a smooth pit: "We picked *plums* to make our own jam."

points (pŏints) **1.** sharp ends. **2.** aims a finger to: "She *points* at what she wants."

pres·i·dent (prez′i dənt) **1.** the highest officer of a company or club. **2.** the head of a government, often with a capital *P*: "The *President* of the United States lives in the White House."

prob·lem (prob′ləm) something difficult to deal with or hard to understand: "I talked over my *problem* with my father, and he helped me to solve it."

proud (prŏud) **1.** thinking well of oneself. **2.** feeling pride or pleasure: "Father was *proud* of my good work."

pueb·lo (pweb′lō) Spanish word for village or people who live in the villages: "The homes in the *pueblo* are built of stone or adobe bricks."

Q

qui·et (kwī′ət) **1.** not noisy: "We must be *quiet* in the library so people can work." **2.** still; not moving.

a fat	ɔi oil	ch chin
ā ape	oo look	sh she
ä car, father	o͞o tool	th thin
e ten	ou out	*th* then
er care	u up	zh leisure
ē even	ur fur	ŋ ring
i hit		
ir here	ə = a *in* ago	
ī bite, fire	e *in* agent	
o lot	i *in* unity	
ō go	o *in* collect	
ô law, horn	u *in* focus	

R

re·turned (ri turnd′) came back to a place: "After school, I *returned* home."

roof (ro͞of *or* roof) the outside top covering of a building: "She fixed the *roof* so the rain will not come in."

roof

S

Sat·ur·day (sat′ər dē *or* sat′ər dā) the seventh day of the week: "The day after Friday is *Saturday*."

screamed (skrēmd) made a loud, sharp cry: "The children *screamed* because they were hurt."

se·ven (sev″n) one more than six: "There are *seven* days in a week."

shad·ow (shad′ō) a dark shape cast by light on an object: "I saw my *shadow* on the wall."

sighed (sīd) took in and let out a long, deep breath: "He heard the news and *sighed*."

shadow

129

skate

sim·ple (sim′p'l) easy to do or understand: ''The spelling test was *simple* for me because I knew all the words.''

skate (skāt) glide or move along wearing skates: ''She will *skate* across the pond.''

skates (skāts) shoes with wheels or blades on them for gliding: ''Josh got new ice *skates* for his birthday.''

slow·ly (slō′lē) **1.** not quickly. **2.** taking a long time: ''Eric was late because he walked home *slowly*.''

smooth·ly (smo͞o*th*′lē) moving evenly or gently: ''The wagon rolled *smoothly* down the road.''

sneak·ers (snē′kərz) shoes with rubber soles and heels worn for play and sports: ''Howard wore his new *sneakers* to play outside.''

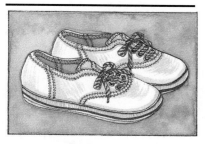
sneakers

snow bank *or* **snow·bank** (snō bañgk) a large mound of snow: ''The car got stuck in a *snow bank*.''

split (split) **1.** separate into parts. **2.** a dance or acrobatic movement in which legs are spread in a straight line with one in front of the body and the other behind, or both legs out to the sides of the body: ''It takes practice to learn to do a *split*.''

stand (stand) **1.** be or get in an upright position. **2.** put up with: ''He couldn't *stand* the pain.''

sto·ries (stô′rēz) **1.** true or made-up tales. **2.** the space or rooms making up one level of a building: ''Our house is three *stories* tall.''

strange (strānj) **1.** unusual; odd: ''She wore a *strange* costume to the party.'' **2.** not familiar; not known, seen, or heard before.

stretch·es (strech′əz) **1.** reaches out. **2.** pulls or draws tight: ''He *stretches* his legs before he runs.''

stretches

stroked (strōkt) rubbed something gently: ''The mother *stroked* her daughter's long hair.''

stud·ent (sto͞od″nt *or* styo͞od″nt) a person who studies; a person who goes to school: "Hannah is a *student* in second grade."

sup·pose (sə pōz′) assume, believe, or think: "I *suppose* you are correct."

swan (swän) a large, graceful water bird with a long, thin, curving neck: "We watched the *swan* glide through the water."

a fat	oi oil	ch chin
ā ape	o͞o look	sh she
ä car, father	o͞o tool	th thin
e ten	ou out	*th* then
er care	u up	zh leisure
ē even	ur fur	n̑g ring
i hit		
ir here	ə = a *in* ago	
ī bite, fire	e *in* agent	
o lot	i *in* unity	
ō go	o *in* collect	
ô law, horn	u *in* focus	

T

---

talk·er (tôk′ər) a person who speaks: "John is a fast *talker*."

taught (tôt) helped to learn; showed how to do something: "He *taught* the dog tricks."

those (*th*ōz) the ones mentioned or pointed out: "*Those* books are mine."

to·night (tə nīt′) on or during this night: "We are going to a party *tonight*."

tortillas (tôr tē′ əs) a thin pancake made of cornmeal or flour; a common food in Mexico: "We ate *tortillas* with our soup."

trem·bling (trem′b′lin̑g) shaking from cold, fear, or excitement: "Jack was so afraid, he was *trembling* all over."

swan

tortillas

U

ugly

ug·ly (ug′lē) not pleasant to look at: "The empty old house was *ugly*."

un·der·stand (un dər stand′) to get the meaning of: "Do you *understand* the answer?"

V

village

vil·lage (vil′ij) a group of houses in the country, smaller than a town: "There are ten houses in our *village*."

132

W

win·ter (win′tər) the season that follows fall; the coldest season: "In many places it snows during the *winter*."

won·der (wun′dər) **1.** a strange or unusual thing or event. **2.** wish to know: "I *wonder* why she called me."

a fat	**oi** oil	**ch** chin
ā ape	**oo** look	**sh** she
ä car, father	**ōo** tool	**th** thin
e ten	**ou** out	**th** then
er care	**u** up	**zh** leisure
ē even	**ur** fur	**ng** ring
i hit		
ir here	**ə** = a *in* ago	
ī bite, fire	e *in* agent	
o lot	i *in* unity	
ō go	o *in* collect	
ô law, horn	u *in* focus	

Y

yeast (yēst) a yellow substance made from a plant, used in baking to make dough rise: "We added *yeast* when we were making the bread."

winter

133

ABOUT THE
Authors & *Illustrators*

HANS CHRISTIAN ANDERSEN

✳ Hans Christian Andersen was born in Denmark. His father was a shoemaker, and his mother was a washerwoman. The family was very poor. When Hans was fourteen years old he could not read or write, but he wanted to learn. He was only able to receive an education when a friend helped him get a royal scholarship. Later he graduated from the University of Copenhagen. He once said that he wanted his stories to be read by "both young and old." *(1805–1875)*

ANN NOLAN CLARK

■ Ann Nolan Clark won the Newbery Medal for her book *Secret of the Andes*. She has also won other awards for her writing. The first books she wrote were about Native Americans. She taught in a one-room school for many years. Her students were Tesuque Pueblo children. Her books are based on real life. She writes about the people she has known and the places she has been. *(Born 1898)*

AILEEN FISHER

▲ Aileen Fisher has written many poems and stories. She has won awards for her writing. Many of her poems and stories are about nature. She says, "I write for children for a very simple reason. I enjoy it. And I usually write about nature for the same reason. My day is not complete unless I have a good walk on a mountain trail with a dog." *(Born 1906)*

LANGSTON HUGHES

✸ Langston Hughes wrote many poems, plays, and songs for both adults and children. He began to write poetry when he was in elementary school after being elected class poet. His first poem was about the teachers and students in the school. "So at graduation, when I read the poem, naturally everybody applauded loudly," he said. "That was the way I began to write poetry." He continued to write as an adult, and he often traveled to different countries to meet new people. Then he would write about them. *(1902–1967)*

JOHANNA HURWITZ

■ Johanna Hurwitz writes books for young people. She is also a children's librarian. She says, "My parents met in a bookstore, and there has never been a moment when books were not important in my life." Johanna Hurwitz writes many letters to friends and relatives. She says, "I am sure the letter writing that I do has been the best type of training for my book writing." *(Born 1937)*

136

RACHEL ISADORA

▲ Before Rachel Isadora began writing and illustrating children's books, she was a ballet dancer. She started dancing professionally when she was eleven years old. In her free time, she drew pictures. After a foot injury, she stopped dancing and started *Max*, her first book. Her books have won many awards.

ARNOLD LOBEL

■ Arnold Lobel wrote and illustrated books for young people. His *Frog and Toad Are Friends* was a Caldecott Honor Book, and *Frog and Toad Together* was a Newbery Honor Book. Arnold Lobel said that he always enjoyed making books for children. One of the things he liked best was being able to change a character that was not acting the way he thought it should act. *(1933–1987)*

LILIAN MOORE

✳ Lilian Moore has taught elementary school and was also an editor for a children's book club. She has written many children's books. She has always loved books. When she was young, she would return from the library with an armful of books, reading all the way home. Even when she was little, she often told stories to others. She says, "I can still remember saying 'to be continued tomorrow!'" As an adult, it seemed natural for her to continue telling stories to others by writing children's books. *(Born 1909)*

CONNIE AND PETER ROOP

▲ Connie and Peter Roop are husband and wife.
When they were children, they each loved to read.
They both say that they often took a flashlight to bed
so that they could read under the covers! Before the
Roops began writing children's books, they were
teachers. They have worked together on a series of
joke and riddle books and several science books.
Keep the Lights Burning, Abbie is based upon a real
story about Abbie Burgess. All by herself, she kept
two lighthouses lit during a month of stormy weather
in 1856! The Roops like to travel, and they learned of
Abbie Burgess when they were traveling off the coast
of Maine. *(Both Born 1951)*

AUTHOR INDEX